SNOWDOG
By Kim Chinquee

flash fictions

Also by Kim Chinquee

Oh Baby
Pretty
Pistol
Veer
Shot Girls
Wetsuit

Works from this collection (some in different forms) have appeared in the following journals: *NOON*, *Conjunctions*, *Matter Press*, *Big Other*, *Linea*, *F(r)iction*, *People Holding*, *Gargoyle*, *Peauxdunque Review*, *Story*, *JMWW*, *New World Writing*, *New Limestone Review*, *Newfound* and *MumberMag*.

Cover design by Joan Wilking

ISBN: 978-1-7351131-5-9
LCCN: 2020944245

First Edition

Published by Ravenna Press
ravennapress.com

To my son, Josh

Contents

SNOWDOG

Part I—*SNOW AND DOGS*

SNOWMAKER

It's ten below. The boyfriend who I live with says the best time to make fake snow is when it's actually snowing. Because of the conditions. He learned that from a snowmaker.

Hmmm, I say. We live across from the big slope.

When I drive by, I see the skiers, like little ants going up on the lifts. It's a highway, so I don't have a lot of time to look. Down the slopes, they seem like little dots in a game of Intellivision I used to play when I was younger.

I've only been on the magic carpet: a kind of escalator that takes people up to the top of the bunny hill.

When I ski, I wear the boots and helmet and goggles, the skis and poles my boyfriend's mom didn't need after she turned seventy. I'm the same size as his mom. She gave her equipment to me seven years ago, months before her son and I broke up, years before her son and I reunited. She's eighty-one now.

Me, I just turned fifty.

I've just come back from Hawaii, visiting my son. He's married now, to a woman with a Southern accent. She leaves him Post-It notes. She cuts potatoes the way he likes. I like her. She has the same first name as me. And now, she has the last name. We are, as far as I know, the only Kim Chinquees.

After arriving home from Hawaii to my boyfriend and our dogs, the thermostat reads sixty. There are dishes in the sink. The dogs bark—since we live in snow country, we call them our snowdogs.

It was my fourth trip to Hawaii. This time, I rode around in a convertible. My son is a soldier. He's infantry.

I stayed at his place, sleeping on the air mattress I bought for him and his wife. I woke a lot of mornings to soldiers marching in cadence, which reminds me of my military time, when my son was a baby.

I ran a lot. I woke to bangs from the shooting range.

I spent a lot of time at the beach. The sun beating on my skin. The feel of the sand under me. The water was enormous, the shore a mouth. I fell asleep to the sound of the waves.

THROUGH THE ICE

We find a long log that's fallen, one that goes across the creek, something that can help us shimmy ourselves and our bikes across to get to the other side.

It's freezing, and my body's already soaked, having fallen through another creek maybe a mile before my boyfriend and I finally got to this place.

After that fall, after getting through and to the other side, when my boyfriend asked if I was OK, I said I just have to keep moving.

I'm wearing a bike helmet, a winter jacket and some snow pants. Wool socks and hiking boots.

After I fell through the ice, and made it up and to the other side, he found me there. He knew better than to ride through and over the ice.

Before I got to that first creek, approaching it with him behind me, I asked, "Should I go? Should I go?"

I asked, "Should I try? Should I try?"

It isn't until hours later, after I finally make it home and stand in the shower, realizing how cold I really am, then dress into clean dry clothes, covering myself with blankets, snuggling with the dogs, that I realize my phone has been on—its lens filming that whole fall— from the inside of my pocket.

BODY PARTS

Wake up! says Raven the dog, standing over us. She puts her nose to mine, then to my boyfriend's, getting between us.

She paws at my face, the pace of her movement gaining in momentum. This stirs the other dogs: Bird, who talks in a whine. Part husky, she sings when she's sad or hurt or hungry. The other dog, our Japanese chin, starts his routine of stepping all over us, and the other one, our papillon mix, gets out from under the bed, hops up and starts his lick. He's fond of the hair on the head of my boyfriend.

I pull the covers over me, trying to get back to my dream of key lime soda, snowstorms, cauliflower crackers, a submarine that flies higher than an airplane.

The playoff continues: Raven digs with her huge paws. Bird speaks. She jumps. Our papillion, Boots, uses his tongue with passion. Our Japanese chin, Spiff, uses us as a treadmill.

I scooch myself under the covers, under this trampoline—this gym class—closer to my boyfriend. His breath is warm, his body strong. I kiss his stubble. I nuzzle myself.

CHOW

"I hear you," I say to our dog, Boots, from behind the door that stands between the bedroom and the kitchen, where I am, with two of our other dogs: filling their dishes, scooping from the big bag of dog food. Boots is a fast eater, chunky, and I imagine his food already gone by now. We have a system for reasons like this one.

Raven, the other dog, the big and young one, is in the bathroom, probably not eating. Probably sitting by the door trying to hear what's going on in the other rooms without her.

The bathroom has two doors: one leading to the kitchen and one leading to the bedroom. The bedroom has two doors: one to the bathroom and another to the kitchen.

The two dogs in the kitchen: our husky mix Bird, and our Japanese chin, Spiff, look up at me. "Eat!" I say, and Bird paws at the water dish, which is empty. It topples.

"Silly," I say, and lift the dish to the sink to fill it.

As the dogs eat and drink, I add water to the vase of sunflowers that were gifted to me by my neighbors' twin grandkids after I made them cookies for their birthday. I finger the stem, and think of my son and his wife, if they are really never having kids like they say. They have a dog named Hazel, and a one-eyed cat named Nip, who is fat from eating all the dog food.

Boots paws at the door again, whines. Spiff and Bird make chopping sounds, their teeth sinking into the hard nuggets. Spiff looks up at me with his big eyes, tilts his head.

"Good boy," I say. He looks like he's smiling.

I head to the bathroom, where Raven is positioning herself, down, with her paws out.

"Eat!" I say. But she doesn't eat much when my boyfriend isn't in the room with her.

"Dad's at work, little girl," I say. I scoop some of her food from her dish on the floor, which sometimes gets her started. I lift one kibble to my mouth, pretend to chew.

"Yum," I say, and she yawns so hard it makes a sounds like a wow.

DOGFIGHT

My car is like a missile in the snowstorm. An all-wheel. A Mercedes.

I've just gotten a haircut, a massage, and my body feels like butter.

The interstate smells of Cheerios. It is Silo City. It smells more like Cheerios than the actual Cheerios you buy and eat from the box. I like driving by the silos, seeing, smelling the factory.

My car needs coolant. It tells me so. I haven't had the car serviced since I bought it in April. My boyfriend sells cars and he got me a deal.

Now it's dark and one below. We survived him buying an old house in the woods, me selling my new home, us moving in, each with our two dogs, into this new one.

We live in snow country. He quit his job on my birthday. He took a week off. He likes to ski. He bought each of us fat bikes.

I still have boxes of books in my car I keep meaning to bring to my office on campus. It's an hour drive. My office is on the third floor and the elevator's been broken.

Snow falls on the windshield. My wipers have sensors so they know how fast to go.

After I slide into the driveway, I gather up the groceries: coffee, peanut butter, honey. Almonds, coconut. Ham.

I open the door to see one of his two dogs greet me—Raven— she's big and white with a dark snout. She sits on my brown sofa by the entrance, with her head down.

One of the stools from the bar has fallen, tipped.

I go upstairs and see his other dog, Bird, behind my desk, standing. She's older. Whiter. Wet.

I see the blood in her ears.

JUST A LITTLE TICKLE

"The fish is so good here," says my boyfriend.

He's eating a taco stuffed with swordfish. I say, "I had that the last time I came here."

My son is having a pork sandwich and his wife, a Caesar salad.

I take a bite of my house salad with its peanut-flavored dressing. Cut a slice of the fish on my plate. "Mmm," I say. "The fish."

A gecko perches on the ledge. "Look," I say. It's a lovely green, its eyes buggy. I put my hands up to try to catch it. The last time I was here, in Hawaii, a gecko lived up in the lamp where I was glamping. Others came and went—on the floors and steps—mostly where the light was. They're fast and I wanted to feel them in my hands, wanted to know what their skin was like, just a little tickle.

"They're everywhere," says my son. "Especially in the field. The centipedes are enormous."

I say, "I saw a picture."

He's infantry, in the army. He spends a lot of time in the remote parts of the island, firing missiles, tossing grenades, using his compass.

"Damn straight," says his wife.

Since my son and his wife got married, his wife and I share a name. Our same first name isn't all that common. When I met my son's dad, before we got married, I'd never met anyone with that surname. I took the name. Even after the divorce from my son's dad, I kept it. I wanted to continue to share it with my son. My daughter-in-law has adopted this same surname, too.

His wife, my daughter-in-law, who I call Junior, is from Alabama. My last time in Hawaii was six months ago for their wedding. The day before I left, we met at this restaurant and they said they had an announcement—she wasn't going back to the mainland. She was staying here with my son. It made perfect sense to me. Right away, they got base housing. That's where they live.

That's where my boyfriend and I are staying, on this visit.

Today, my son and his wife took us to a beach where my boyfriend learned how to surf—I'd bought him the lesson for Christmas. My son, my daughter-in-law and I sat at the beach and soaked in sun, read some books. My daughter-in-law and I stood at the shoreline and tried finding special seashells. The waves were rough and seemed to push us away, then suck us in again, and I tried to find my boyfriend further out, occasionally seeing him in his red-white-and-blue trunks, being pulled along by his instructor.

At one point, my daughter-in-law had to run to the 7-11 to buy tampons. I told her I'd give her some, if I had them. I had a hysterectomy months before.

My son took her to the store. They returned later with smokes and a sandwich.

Here, the gecko disappears. I eat my salad. Take a sip of wine. My son and his wife talk about exchanging bites with each other. They negotiate. "One bite of mine but don't eat too much of it," she says. She cuts up some chicken. She takes a bite of his sandwich. "That's a big fucking bite!" he says.

My boyfriend looks into his smartphone, probably seeing if he has any "likes" of his surfing pictures on Facebook. He hands me his phone, which reveals a picture of our dogs. Raven and Bird and Spiff and Boots, giving the camera their attention. I took that picture. I'd asked them to sit for treats.

My boyfriend says, "I miss them."

"Aww," I say. "Our little snowdogs."

My son and his wife look and they say, "Cute." They talk about their own dog. All our dogs are rescues.

My boyfriend continues scrolling through his phone.

I see mountains in the distance, remember my last time here, how the sky lit up with rainbows.

The place is called Breakers, with a surfing theme: boards everywhere, with pictures of surfers, the legends. Aloha and Mahalo. Hang loose!

I offer my boyfriend the rest of my swordfish.

I take off my glasses. I think of the icicles probably making themselves at home from the roof of our house. We hired a friend of ours to stay. To take care of our dogs, who I miss too.

I look at my son. He wears a ring. His skin, so smooth. His face. His eyes, his lips, aglow.

I say, "The fish is so good here."

A DOG NAMED WOOF

We're in base housing, with its cinder block walls. Like the first bases when I was military, where I lived with my then-husband, when my son wasn't even born yet. After the divorce, I stayed in the Air Force, moving from one base to the next, taking my son with me. We had a dog named Woof, and since I was moving to England, I left Woof with the ex. Woof ran off one day. My ex lived on a highway.

Now my son's twenty-eight. He lives with his wife and dog and cat on this lovely Hawaiian base, with candlenut and mangrove trees, ones where soldiers, like my son, march with their backs full of rucksacks.

They drive around in Humvees carrying rifles.

It's illegal to kill chickens in Hawaii.

In certain parts of this state, tourists pay a lot of money just to wear leis on their necks.

BOOTS IS A LOVER

"Wait in line," I say to the four dogs.

"Sit," I say to Raven, who is clearly the alpha.

She gets down and wiggles. She's the biggest of the four, maybe sixty pounds, with a white body and a brown snout. I put the prong collar around her, and it's always a hassle, trying to get the prongs into their right places. It's a strain on my fingers.

Bird is next. A husky mix. My boyfriend called her Bird because she likes to sprawl herself on the floor, like she has wings. When she runs away, it's like she's flying. She's a talker, the first to wake us in the morning, with her yowl, yowl, yowl. Sometimes I talk back to her, yowling myself.

Boots is a lover. He's my boy, mostly papillion, according to the Rescue. He's brown and white and round, with a tall fluffy tail, upright ears and a large snout. He licks a lot. He sleeps under the bed at night, sits by the door during the day, but at any other time, he's the biggest one to cuddle.

Spiff usually is the last to get the leash on. He's apprehensive when I use a tone that's firm. He's a Japanese chin. Catlike. He likes to lick the others in order to groom them. He barks. He gets on the back of the sofa a lot, and at night, he sleeps by my head, on the pillow.

My boyfriend keeps calling Spiff a she, probably because he's always had girl dogs. And Spiff, he says, always acts so girl-like.

After all the leashes are connected, before I go out, I make sure to have poop bags in my pocket. I wear a coat, a hat, and I don my galoshes.

THE DOG SMELLS LIKE PEPPERMINT

The dog smells like peppermint, he says, before fucking me on the kitchen table, my backbone pressing up against the edge that will leave me bruised days after I show him the petunias I planted in our garden, the herbs and the tomatoes, me touching him in places with what he calls my greenest thumb.

SNOWSTORM

The two older daughters were left with the babies. They splashed in our neighborhood pool, the daughters in their bikinis, the babies drooling and crying and babbling. The daughters were slim in their suits, their long hair slick, and I wondered if they realized how beautiful they were, if they thought of their lives ahead. I was new to the pool. New to the neighborhood. I moved here with my boyfriend and our dogs in the middle of a snowstorm. He owned the house. I focused on my work. I had books to write. My life, since I moved here, seemed like a merry-go-round of where I lived now and where I lived before. Some days, I felt I was made of plastic. I focused on the children. Their limbs in the pool, how they moved. My son was in the army. He used to grab onto my hand. This pool seemed kind of snow-like. I was cold. I watched the girls. They put the babies in the water, dunking them and then raising them up again.

FOXY

"I guess we're not having any babies," I say to my boyfriend. He's driving my Mercedes. His left arm's in a sling.

I reposition myself, pull the seatbelt so it isn't binding.

He says, "We can always buy one."

The traffic is thick; a limo pulls beside us. I imagine a queen. A wedding. Being someone's bride once. My ex driving me home from the hospital with our newborn. It was hot in Mississippi. My baby was Caesarean. I was twenty-one then.

My boyfriend says, "There are all kinds. Black and white and brown and red. We might have some choices."

He leans forward so the hand of his slinged arm can reach the knob so he can turn the signal.

He says, "We missed you. The dogs went nuts last night. I think they saw some foxes."

"Foxy," I say. I imagine the hammock in the yard, the boxes in the house, still unpacked, ones with games like Clue and Hangman. Pictures of my son. Our bikes. His accident. Finding him last week in shock, his shoulder out of socket. His bike twisted. We live in the woods and he was stuck there.

My surgery was set for nine a.m. It had nothing to do with his accident. We have four dogs between us. Once, years ago, before we broke up and got back together, I thought that I was pregnant.

The surgery was complicated. No one came to see me. People have to work.

My son called. I imagined him inside my womb. Growing. Waking. Gone. He's twenty-eight. He's serving in the army.

I bled a lot. I had low respirations. I was a hard case. My uterus was taken. I didn't know the difference until my doctor told me.

Last week, in urgent care, my boyfriend sat on the table, shirtless, letting the assistant touch him. She moved his arms. I hated seeing him hurt like that. This is not like us. We are active. We are athletes.

We met running. We bike. We snowshoe and we ski. We take care of our snowdogs.

I had to help him dress. I had to help him shower.

Today, the nurse had to wheelchair me down to the car when he came to get me.

He veers onto an exit. There's a bump in the road.

OUR DOG RAN DOWN THE HIGHWAY

He came in from work, carrying firewood. He smelled like the string cheese I put in his lunches. I packed a lunch for him every single day, after cooking him oatmeal for breakfast. I prepared dinner, too.

I also had a career. It was a super long drive, which wasn't exactly a picnic.

He put down the wood and bit my neck. He grabbed my boob and felt it.

The record player I'd just unpacked was broken and behind us.

What are you doing? I said.

Molesting you, he said.

Oh, no, I said. You're not.

MAKE IT WIGGLE

I wake up missing my big toe. I try to make it wiggle.
    It's kind of a relief.
    My boyfriend, in his mullet days, kept having low potassium.
    Or maybe: was that me?
    He eats donuts. Shepherd pies.
    The dogs bark.
    From time to time, he spoons me.
    He wakes with gout, his right foot twice its already unusual size.

SNOW THE BLOW

Do you hear the rain? I say when waking him at midnight. The sound drums on the roof like a heartbeat.

Twist your tongue, I say.

We kiss. He tastes like cherries and rum.

He's better than a paycheck.

Plant the pansy in the pumpkin, he says.

Dog the hog. Snow the blow. Toot the tot, root the rot.

Eat me like I'm cheesecake.

I lick his neck and he pops me like thunder.

I START TO UNLEASH

"I'm going to have my boss killed," he says as he comes through the door.

I've just taken our four dogs out. I say, "Your girl is insecure again. She tried to bite a kid."

He says, "My boss is an asshole."

As I start to unleash the dogs, they bark and jump. He tells them they are good.

I say, "I can be an asshole too."

"Yeah," he says, "but not consecutively."

PART II—DOODLE

GOLDENDOODLE

Jim's dog is going nuts again. Pacing the back, by the kitchen, then the extra bedroom, which he'd made into a closet. Then to the front, to the porch, where Jim's girlfriend Elle found a portrait of Jim and his ex. It's in the cabinet, open. She hasn't noticed it until now. She figures maybe Jim's ex-wife brought it over, when the ex came to bring the dog, since the ex was leaving town again. Elle couldn't help but see the portrait. It's a nice portrait, Jim looking younger, thin, though older than when Elle had met him. She's known him longer than the ex. Elle met Jim in high school. They were sweethearts. After Jim's divorce, Elle and Jim reunited.

The dog's a goldendoodle. Elle can't help but like him, love him, really.

As the tea brews, she looks out at the neighbors, their shit all over the yard. Ornaments, and in the driveway is a dumpster. A white rusty truck that's noisy just sitting there. Elle's encountered the neighbors more times than she's liked: the woman who never wears a bra, her breasts sagging beneath her stained shirts. A guy, possibly her husband? Always sitting on his lawn chair by his fire, his gut hanging, tattoos on his back and arms and belly, his gray hair in a tail. And another man who hardly says much, using all his fingers to entertain yet another litter of new puppies.

Elle lives in another state. Since she and Jim reunited, they're doing things long-distance. She's teaching classes online for the summer, so it only makes sense—in order for them to be together—according to him (he works at a bank), for her to spend these months at his house.

Just yesterday, a few days after arriving, Jim had shown her how to use his rifle. How to load it, aim it, cock it. She was in the army. She knows how to shoot. He gave her a refresher. He showed her where he stores the ammo. She has good aim. Jim says he will protect her. Yesterday, when he said that, she laughed a little, pointed her finger at him, saying, Boom!

Does she love him? She isn't the same girl she was in high school.

She sighs.

Jim's at work.

The dog squirms. She tells the dog to take it easy. She grabs the leash, attaches it, and takes them out for a romp again.

CHASERS

Jim and Elle decide not to bathe the dog and Jim takes her to Chasers, a bar with a dance floor and pool tables. Signs promoting Bud and Miller, Nascar. Things seem quiet, stale, and besides Jim and Elle, inside Chasers, there's only a bartender and two smokers (actually smoking) who look like they won't live a whole lot longer. The bartender is tan and big-muscled, with white hair and a mustache. Jim orders a Bud Light and Elle gets a Bloody Mary. She has to use the bathroom. It's clean, and looking in the mirror sends her shocks: to think she's with this guy from high school. Back then she only wanted to impress him.

She smiles at herself. She looks pretty good for being over forty.

When she goes back out, everyone else is gone besides Jim and the bar guy. Jim says, "I did a shot."

He loves Jameson.

Elle has a colleague who drinks Jameson. They're friends. She wonders what her friends in New York are up to. Home. It looks nothing like this place in the middle of Wisconsin.

A guy comes in with his helmet, talks about his parents' corgi, how he hit it with his cycle. Damn it, he says. He's a roadie, and says the newspaper is reporting things about him again.

Jim says, "I haven't heard anything." He lights up a smoke himself.

Elle says to the roadie, "I'm not from here."

The roadie has a triangular beard, missing teeth.

He says to Jim, "Are you a cop?"

Jim says, "I'm not a cop. Why do people think that?"

Jim's hair is clean-cut. He wears expensive glasses. He's a bank manager.

The roadie rambles on about how he hit a deer once, went flying to the bushes. He didn't have insurance, and the helicopter bill was enormous. He orders some kind of shot.

Elle finishes her Bloody. She asks Jim, "Can we go?"

Jim slams his drink. He says, "What a bar."

Outside, as he starts the car, Elle says, "That place is a photograph."

WILDCAT

They're going to the mountain. He let his ex-wife borrow his GPS, so the three of them just wing it: Elle and Jim and the dog named Doodle. Jim says he knows the way, driving through Viroqua, Westby, Cashton, places where he has to drive for work, towns big on farming and the Amish. Hills. Most of the towns are Norwegian.

Elle sits there in his Blazer. Doodle, in the back, with his paws on the compartment between them. Doodle pants, looking happy. The sunroof's open, and the windows. The wind blows in. Jim drives around the bends and up them. He knows where he's going. Every now and then he lights a smoke, holding the wheel with his elbows. Trust me, he says. We're going to the mountain.

When his phone gives off his brother's ringtone (some kind of cowboy theme) he flips it, says, Oy, hoy! And talks about the trip, about how he's loaned his GPS to the ex, saying he's probably too nice of an ex, that it probably pisses off Elle.

Elle looks at Jim then, his one cigarette hand on the wheel, one hand with his phone, at his head that's balding. At his lips. He has nice lips. She's always loved his lips. His eyes. His eyes are blue.

They end up in a place called Norwalk. They seem far from any mountain. There's a bar with a Schlitz sign. The bar is called The Thing. They leave Doodle in the Blazer with the sunroof open. Jim needs some direction. Maybe someone in the bar can help.

At The Thing, Jim orders a Bud Light for himself and Elle can't decide what she wants. She orders what's was on tap.

The bartender looks about the size of a dozen people and when Jim asks how he is, he says, "Living the dream! Every day's a holiday! Every paycheck is a fortune!"

The Thing is old and dingy. A tavern, really, like the ones Elle knew as a girl in the town called Advance, which now is owned by the neighbors of her childhood.

Here, there's a pool table and a jukebox, a picture of two Bud girls in tight tops and long hair, their boobs almost touching. A sign

offering a So-Cone, and a swirl, a girl at the end of the bar with
leathery skin and frazzled hair and a cigarette says her name is
Wendy. The other old and toothless bartender asks Jim and Elle
where they're from, so they provide the same story they present to
everyone these days: she lives in New York and he lives in Viroqua.
They are high school sweethearts who have reunited.

The bartender says, "That's sweet."

He writes out directions to the mountain. He says, "You're lost.
You'll have to pass the meat plant. You'll know it when you're there.
It smells bad."

When Jim and Elle finally arrive, Jim drives to the top. He didn't
follow the bartender's directions. Rather, he drove back to Cashton,
where he and Elle stopped at a lunch place where he always goes
when he's working in that office. There, he had a Bloody Mary and
a chaser and Elle sipped her beer, too full to even drink it. They got
some water in a bowl and brought it out to Doodle, and Jim said he
had a bad feeling about the mountain, that something in his gut told
him not to go there, that he had to protect them.

He says, I should have brought my rifle.

At the park's office, Jim gets a sticker to put on the Blazer to last
for the summer. He also gets some info on the campground and
canoeing. While he does that Elle waits in the car with Doodle,
sighing every now and then, thinking of her home back in New York,
probably getting dusty. The bills. The rent. Her obligations as a
teacher. Her back feels knotted. The dog drools.

When they find a spot and get out, Jim puts Doodle on his
leader. Doodle runs to a bush and smells it. He lifts his leg and pees.

Jim and Elle follow a path, a trail that's marked off so no one
can drive there. Jim says, "We finally made it."

Jim says, "We're making memories."

Elle walks with him to the top and looks down at the view, at
the trees, the valleys, the homes.

Everything. So far away and distant.

OLD TOAST

He has not walked the dog again. This becomes my job. I've told him I don't mind. He has the dog part-time—he has me part-time. The dog stays with his ex when she doesn't have to travel, and I stay here when I'm not teaching. I travel miles to come here.

The dog's already back on the bed, knowing since he didn't get a walk from my boyfriend, I'll be the one to take him. Some nights, if the dog is on the bed, he pants so loud the bed shakes.

Cheese, I say to the pup. Though his name is Doodle. My work involves trying to do better for my classes. I have the summer off. I write stuff. I have the freedom, and make more money than my boyfriend. He's some kind of bank manager. He's got to be to work at eight, but he always gets in early, saying he has to set an example. When he wakes, he does his bear growl, then I hear him between my many snoozes, him in the shower, and I can smell the lingering scent of him smoking. Before he leaves, he comes in, where I'm halfway sleeping, him in his ties and pants, saying he has to make the donuts.

Today I get up, looking at Doodle. I think of the fight from two nights before, when I'd asked my boyfriend to read a proposal I'd written and he said he could teach me something. I was only trying to share. I didn't like his idea. He said I could make millions with his game plan. He said that he could help me.

I make the coffee. I make my same old toast. I've been at this place for two months, and I think about my home in New York, what I might do if I were there, on my own, whose shirts I would iron, whose lawn I would mow, whose dinners I'd be making. Things I'd do for myself.

I take Doodle, putting on his leader. I don my sandals, and promise him brats on the grill. Oops, I say. The grill is broken. I'm still in my pajamas. We walk to the end of the road. We take a shortcut through the ditch to get back again.

AIRFARE

It's almost midnight and the day is one thing, then another: a road trip to the airport, then waiting for her plane, which the attendant said was stuck in a hailstorm in Nebraska. A team of dancers doing cartwheels by the window, where the planes looked like the planes of all the old days. Her first leg was Detroit. The airport changed, it seemed, maybe less than she had, since her first time was in high school: going to Hawaii with her girlfriend, her pining over Jim, then later when she left to join the Air Force, then marriage and divorce, her driving her son to airports in Chicago and New Orleans, Minneapolis, and Houston, so he could see his father, not old enough to fly on his own then—all those times that blurred like this one would, most likely, even with pictures. The tunnel annoyed her—with its flashing neon lights, a voice that kept saying the walkway is ending.

It's her choice to go now. She's been staying with her boyfriend, Jim, at his home in Wisconsin. It's been two months, and there she longed for something he couldn't give: was it her apartment? With her things? Her place is small. But it's hers. She's worked so hard to get there.

On the flight from Detroit to New York, she imagines Jim, just home from his bank job. Maybe walking Doodle. Maybe with his case of Bud, unloading it into his beer fridge. He's probably changing back into his house clothes, which he does in the extra room, which they call their closet. He wears briefs. He'll be taking off his tie, hanging it right there on the tie rack. His shirt, which she's ironed, in the basket. His pants, hanging them just right, and he'll get out one of the many t-shirts that he bought in the tropics, one she's probably washed and folded. If she were there, he'd kiss her and she might take his hand and lead him to the bedroom.

He was sitting on the sofa when Elle told him, "I need to go home. Just maybe for the weekend."

He was just home from work, in his Pensacola t-shirt. It was a sober night for him, and those nights he was quiet and reflective. He said, "Honey, but I love you."

After her plane lands, she tells herself, "You're home now."

It's dark, and clean rain splatters.

Her apartment is empty, save her bed and sofa. A chair, the kitchen set, the TV. Stuff. Her desk is old and clunky. Her place is cleaner than she remembered. Before she left, she scrubbed it, scrubbed it, scrubbed.

She falls back on her bed, looks up at the fan, still on, and the bleach smell lingers.

PART III—*BE NICE TO THE ANIMALS*

BE NICE TO THE ANIMALS

Be nice to the animals, is what I imagine my aunt saying, up wherever she exists now.

After my grandfather died (on my mom's side), I'd consulted with her (she was alive then), because I had a trip planned to Key West. Should I go back to Wisconsin for his funeral? Or should I take the trip that my long-distance former-high-school-boyfriend-then-current-boyfriend had planned for us to Key West?

I remembered sitting somewhere, maybe the airport, on the phone with her, and she said, You already said goodbye. I imagine heaven a place with all the animals. Dogs and cats. Maybe even turkeys.

I went to Key West. That was ten years ago, I paid tribute to my grandfather. He was a fisherman. My boyfriend then chartered us a boat and we caught small fish, put them in the boat that we later used for shark bait.

When the captain brought us to a shallow section, we waited like statues. The whole expanse of the water was like a clear manicured lawn.

The sharks started to swarm in. They lingered. They were handsome.

I wore a harness. Once they came closer, I baited one and hooked him. It took me an hour—using the strength of my whole body—to get the shark near enough for a picture. I touched him with my hand and then let him go again.

LUCKY

I walk across the street, bringing the Sangria I concocted, the vegan chocolate truffles, the banana bread I made for the first time without eggs. I have fun baking and cooking stuff that is presumed to be healthy.

I see these people often, waving to them across the road, or when I walk my dog, Luck, passing them on the sidewalk. Until this, I hadn't been invited to their parties. One of our neighbors is moving: the family directly across from me. They've lived here for two years. They had their house built, ground up, like the rest of us.

I enter through the open garage, saying hi to the guy who owns that home. Then hello to the guy who lives on the other side of me—I haven't seen him in months. He was away on assignment. Inside, I put down my food and say hello to all the people. I'm fashionably late. Another neighbor lady I know says, Pour yourself a beverage.

She lives across the street, a few lots over. She's retired, and her husband is disabled. Sometimes I see her in the morning, walking her dog in her pajamas.

They are doctors, lawyers. Business owners. One guy's an electrician. Some of us are teachers.

We're in many ways alike, though maybe different by our hair and skin. By our preferences and sizes. By probably our blood types and sleep patterns and the things we like to eat and with whom we choose to partner.

This is a brand new street. A brand new neighborhood. All of us are new here.

One neighbor says to me, You're ripped.

I say, I'm an athlete! I'm a farm girl.

I talk to the neighbor who lives on my close side. Then to my other neighbor, and another neighbor, who says, Isn't this lovely, what we have here?

I say, How'd I get so lucky!?

Another says, Your grass is so damn green.

The builder had someone put in oak trees in the parkway last October. They looked dead. I asked the guy who planted my tree if it was alive, and whose responsibility is it?

I watered it by default. I had patches in my grass, filled them in with seed, so I went out there with my sprinkler.

I'm here with my neighbors, drinking wine and toasting.

I used to kill every plant I owned.

I tell everybody thank you.

REINDEER

As my neighbors toast, I look at the blinking reindeer on the mantel, its nose kind of orange-like.

"To sportsmanship," says Greg. He's tall and bearded, wears a green tie and a beret.

"Friendship," says Sara, who wears her plaid sweater with its wide red sleeves.

"Kinship," says George, who looks a lot like Santa.

"Marksmanship," says Clara, holding her long-haired Chihuahua, with its crooked glittered bow.

"Courtship," says the man who's come with Clara.

The fireplace hums, though no flames rise and no heat is coming from it. The place smells like peppermint and ginger.

I raise my glass like the others and think about a cruise ship named Fairy, where I'll be the day after tomorrow, sitting on the deck in a bikini, drinking cocktails with one of my two lovers.

"Cruise ship!" I say.

Outside, snow is falling.

The dog barks, Santa laughs and someone says ho.

LUCK

I hold my dog on my arm, like a trophy, up to the guests on my deck: so many neighbors, who I attempt not to make my strangers.

They fill their mouths with slabs of melon that came from my garden. Tomatoes, peppers, broccolini. I put out other goods like cheese. Pieces I've arranged so nicely at the table, with toothpicks, forks, stuff for them to pick at.

My dog starts to collapse. His mouth foams. I can't find his tongue. He pees on me, spills on someone's handbag.

His paws curl and his body trembles.

Luck, I say. His tail is in a spasm.

Luck! I say, to everyone around me.

SIT

Forty minutes in, and I'm looking at my watch. My feet in my shoes lock into pedals of my bike hooked up to my trainer: the front tire doesn't move, propped up on a phone book, the back tire spinning with resistance. The trainer has legs and things that screw.

My coach says to keep resistance low, to keep my RPMs up. I can feel the wheels spin. Today he has assigned me for two hours, which means I'm not even halfway there yet.

My dog sits at the doorway.

Here in my new home, I think of wine glasses, potted plants, this newness which allows me a basement and places for candles, brooms, my custom Adirondack chairs. I am not a cheapskate.

I listen to music on my iPod, studying a poster I tacked to a piece of wood that supports the stairwell. The poster says, "Relentless," and features a star runner who won the Boston Marathon when I was a toddler. I bought the poster almost a year ago and asked that man to sign it. I had to wait in line to see him. When it came my turn, we talked about injuries and where and who I am. He said we're all alike. He said to not forget that.

That was the day before the bombs. I didn't go there to run. I was a block away, at an outside table, eating lettuce, having stopped on my way to the finish line because I was hungry.

I still see people running and screaming and screaming and running and the boom boom boom of it all.

Here, I readjust, and lean, moving my legs, feeling the pressure mostly in my seat parts.

I give in. I commit.

I sit and spin. I use my muscles and make myself stay.

BEAGLE

The woman gets out of the car and asks, Are you OK?

She has long dark hair and sunglasses. I'm trying to get up, but my shoes are still clipped to my bike, and I'm trying to get out of them. I say, Maybe you can help me?

I smell gasoline. A sprinkler sprinkles water on the sidewalk.

I slip my foot out of my shoe, get up and say, I'm OK.

The light has turned green. I lift my bike, hope I didn't hurt it. I bought it less than an hour ago from a store where a man sized me. It's an upgrade. The last bike I bought used from a girl in the middle of a breakup.

I look at her car and say, I think your car's okay. I'm sorry I fell into it.

There's a smear on it, a grease spot.

The car takes off, and I see a line behind her.

I take inventory of the damage. I have a scrape on my knee and on my elbow. My arm hurts.

My bike seems free of damage.

I look around for the beagle that ran in front of me, but I don't see any dog now.

I get back on and ride one block to the park, where I will do two-mile loops, testing out the gears, the aero bars, shifting up the hills, then down them.

I see more dogs there, walking with their owners.

My bike is black, with red tape on the bars and handles. Pretty tires. The bike is handsome. Masculine, I've decided. Definitely a he. I think of what to name him.

SHRINK

My new shrink is old. I've already been through a couple since I moved here. I move a lot. I know what I want.

This one wears nice jewelry with her nails always polished. She probably has a shrink herself. One of my best friends is a shrink. She lives far away. Sometimes she tells me of her clients.

It's all about the intake. I talk about my history. My insurance only covers some things.

The last shrink was a man who just nodded. He used to work in a prison. He was fat. He wasn't in practice for as long as me. I didn't want to teach him.

The one before him told me about her kids. I didn't care about her kids. Well, maybe I did, but it's not why I saw her.

This one asks me questions. She asks about my father. She writes things down in longhand. I imagine it loopy. Her hands are long. I imagine her going home to some nice boyfriend, husband maybe. Lover. Grandkids! Dogs! Or maybe she goes home to her own self, where she cooks something steamy, and goes to bed early.

It always takes me a while to get there.

RESCUE

Even the streetlights suffocate the night, Ellen says to her dog's dead body as she drives down the road. It is ten below, the street's so caked with snow that the movement of the tires make creaking noises as they move over the road. Ellen turns the radio up. Something horn and flute. Even the snowplows suffocate the night, she says, looking at the plow ahead of her, with its big wide rump, knowing the enormous mouth on the front of it. Her dog was twelve years old. Her dog was a Chihuahua. Her dog weighed seven pounds. Ellen turns right, to a street that really isn't plowed well. The road is narrow, with cars parked along one side of it. Even my headlights suffocate the night, Ellen says to her Chihuahua. Ellen's Chihuahua's name was Elle. Ellen has been with Elle for seven years. Ellen takes a left, to a busier street, passing a 711, then a Target, where she used to buy a lot of dog treats. Where she bought a leash and then a dog bed. Shirts and sweaters, jackets that Elle always tried to squirm her way out of. Ellen looks at the bag on the passenger's side. The bag is black. She put the body in it. Ellen found the body on the dog bed. She'd told Elle the night before, "Get out of my bed." She told Elle she needed sleep. "Get out," she had said, like her father used to. Like her mother and her sister and her husband who never really was a husband and then became an ex. When Ellen scolded Elle, Elle would duck her head, like Ellen used to until she didn't anymore. Elle would not get down until Ellen picked her up and moved her. Ellen got her from a rescue. Elle's last owner died. Now Ellen drives in circles. At a red, she finally stops. She picked up Elle's body when she found it. She smelled it, hugged it, kissed. She held her dog. She cradled and she rocked.

DOG-LIKE

The day her after dog dies, Ellen wakes, makes herself some coffee, trying to look out.

She sees dirt in her apartment: on a corner of the floor, a corner of the cabinet, the corner by the dog bed.

She gets out the Windex, and a roll of paper towels.

Ellen squirts and wipes.

Later she drives to Pier One, thinking maybe she'll buy something for the patio. She buys wine glasses that are painted with kites. Most of her inventory's broken.

She drives to another parking lot, walking to the spice store, seeing people on the sidewalk, walking dogs: short and tall, and some of them fat. Some dogs with short snouts, most of them long. She sees a couple spaniels. She follows the path to the pet store, where she used to take her dog since he was a puppy. There she sees a lady with a boy, pulling the leash of a dog that looks a lot like hers did. The dog is dark and longhaired.

Ellen says, Is that your dog?

She pets the dog. She looks at the base of the dog's ear. Her dog had a lump there that had gotten larger, larger, then so large, too large, bigger, huge, humongous.

The lady takes the dog, picks it up, grabs the boy's hand and exits.

Ellen's dog was Elle. She was no cocker spaniel. The first day Elle moved in, the dog went to each room, smelling the floors, hopping on the chairs, putting her nose to the windows. She wagged her tail. She jumped in Ellen's arms, licked Ellen's face and Ellen laughed and told her to stop acting so dog-like.

BUSTER

She set the oven to three-fifty, sprinkling some of the dough with pepperoni, some without, keeping them separate. "These are for me," she'd told her new boyfriend Jim, pointing to the cheese ones. She added mushrooms as he sat there eating the Chex Mix that her mother had made for her last Christmas, feeding some to the cocker spaniel that he'd bought for her that day, bringing him in with a bow on his collar. "Ruff, ruff," Jim had said, and she kissed him, then the puppy. That was days before and they were still trying to find a name that seemed to suit, one day calling the pup Beep, since, when he whined, he sounded like a car horn. But the next day, she said he didn't look like a beep and what kind of name is that, for somebody's puppy?

The puppy was like the one with her ex-husband, another all black cocker that left trails of blood on the carpet, that the vet had said might make it—she'd shot syringes of Pedialite into his mouth—then at two a.m., she sensed something was wrong, and she got up and held him. Buster, she'd said, Buster—how she watched him twitch and end. How, in her arms, dead, he didn't feel much different, how that had surprised her, how she'd stayed there, rocking.

Pretzel, she said.

Jim was feeding the dog a pretzel.

We could call him Pretzel.

He said he didn't look like a pretzel.

She opened the oven door, sliding the sheet in. The puppy barked.

I shouldn't be feeding him pretzels, Jim said. He always fed his own dog–a goldendoodle named Doodle who lived with his ex-wife on the weekday–stuff like popcorn, pizza.

He tossed the puppy a stuffed penguin with a squeaker. The dog bit and pawed, tearing an ear off.

HABITUAL

In the waiting room, I sit in the chair closest to her office. After she calls me in, I'll find the sofa opposite her chair, and I'll see a bookshelf to the left, with texts on depression and co-dependence, addiction and how to feel loved. A window will be to my right. She keeps the blinds closed. I'll hear cars zoom.

Some days, she'll just listen. Some days, she'll get out her machine that I'll put on my lap and as she takes me back to a place that's really hurt me, she'll ask me how I feel. She'll tell me to let my eyes follow the dots. After a while, she will stop, and ask me how I feel again, writing on her notepad. She'll ask me to continue.

I've told her many things. I've lived a lot of places. I'll tell anyone anything about me, as long as he or she will listen.

She has red hair, a tinny voice. She isn't skinny. But she also isn't fat. She's kind of big-chested. Her son is eight, borderline autistic. She went on leave last year because of migraines, then got in a car accident, and had to learn how to write again.

I've practiced therapy for years. With each place I've moved, I searched for someone new—kind of like having to find your favorite stylist when you're somewhere else again, just because.

A friend recommended her. My friend doesn't come here anymore. She says she's poor. She lost her job. She's the kind of friend who mostly cancels plans. I haven't seen her in a while. Lately I've started wondering if she was ever a friend in the first place.

I look at the clock on the shelf. I've been here ten minutes. I wonder if I have the time right. I haven't always been good about keeping plans myself.

Here, I try to be on time. Here, she usually isn't. Members of my family used to say, if one was late, they were on "Elle" time. My name is Elle. I've gotten a lot better and finally told all of them to stop it.

So I am patient with her late-ness. I wait, hearing the chime of my phone, a text from my ex-husband, asking if I've heard from our son. Our son is twenty-five. He lived with me most his life.

I text back and say, He's fine.

I don't say he almost got arrested. Or maybe he did. I'm unsure about some things.

After focusing my eyes on that machine, following the dots, and then the processing and talking, sometimes I'll feel things in my body. Sensations. I've read the research, what it does to the left brain and the right one. I've returned, so vividly, at times, to that little girl I think maybe I was once.

Finally, my therapist comes out. Her hair a mess, her whole self looking flustered.

Oh! she says. I fell asleep. I'm sorry.

I say, Shall I come back?

No, she says. She invites me in. She says, I've been sleeping with the dog at my sister's.

She starts to cry. She talks about family court, her husband's excess touching.

I think to remind her to go to her safe place. I'm not sure what she needs, but I know she needs something.

WEAR YOUR SEATBELT

When I was a kid, there were no seatbelt laws. I'd ride in the back seat of the car with my sister. My dad driving, my mom in the passenger's seat. I remember one day in particular, after church, my sister asking again if we could get a dog, my mom pointing out a neighbor's house to the right of us. She said, That neighbor has depression. That sounded like such an awful thing. Like, who would be so sad? That it needs a label? All I did was ride in the backseat of the car, with my sister. We were quiet. At church, we sang the hymns we were supposed to. This was before my father's breakdown. Before he ended up in the psychiatric ward. He was always the one driving. After the ride that day, at home, mosquitos nipped at my ankles and my mom made caramel corn. New gravel had just been dumped onto our driveway. My mom always said to wear your seatbelt. Wear your seatbelt. Wear your seatbelt. Wear your seatbelt.

IN THE WINDOW

The guy next to me at the cafe has a lot of questions. Like what kind of pasta are you eating? What's that on your skin? I say get away, good god, and good Lordy. He says, are your earrings a big sign?

Sign of what?

He says, I got your attention.

How much for that doggie in the window?

I touch my face. Raise a finger to my earlobe.

Go back to my book about self-healing. Find my feelings. Screw my luck.

LADY AND THE TRAMP

I'm holding my Diet Coke, and he's fingering a French fry. Everything's red in us: the car's exterior, its interior. Me. It's our first date and we're on our way to the drive-in. He drives his dad's old car and it's like everything is many years behind us. Behind the wheel, he reminds me the car is a 1958. A Plymouth Fury.

He's a senior. I'm a freshman. It's my first date ever. He's given me the *Shawano Evening Leader,* said to pick a movie.

It's 1983.

He's kind of hot. I'm new to the public school, having just finished eighth grade at St. Paul's Lutheran, where I was salutatorian, and my childhood sweetheart was valedictorian only by a fraction. I held hands with him once, on the bus, and he used to leave notes in my desk, along with pictures of cute puppies, squares of Bubble Yum. I kissed another boy, one time, in the woods—we used to have little meet-ups, people having people over after school in town so we could learn what it felt like to kiss, feel parts of other people's bodies. We told our parents we were together doing extra homework.

But this is new territory. I'm on a date with Jimmy, and he has his license. And a car! And we've driven to Green Bay, which is miles away.

My mom lives in Green Bay now. I'm still staying at the farm, with my dad, until the end of the semester. My dad had a breakdown at church at St. Paul's on the Fourth of July, sitting next to me, and then my algebra teacher took him and my mom to the hospital while my sister and I sat there for the rest of the service.

It's kind of thrilling to be here in this car with this guy who is much older and is probably on his way to do something else with his life after graduation. I don't know what it's going to be like for me, after moving. I live on a farm. With dairy cows and goats and a dog and tons of kittens. It's been in the family for over a hundred years.

Soon, it will be auctioned. My dad's parents, since he's kind of sick, and my mom's divorcing him, and I'm moving in with her, have decided to disown me.

I'm so nervous. I don't know which movie to choose. I've only been to a couple other movies: *Mary Poppins* and *Lady and the Tramp*. I have lots of chores to do on the farm. And with cross country, going to church, and homework, and 4-H, I really don't get out much.

We've gone through the McDonald's drive-through. He said he was starving. I look at the paper, and choose the movie *Christine*.

"Nice choice," he says, wiping his hands on a napkin.

We sit in the back of the drive-in, and I don't know what to say. The car in the movie looks just like Jimmy's. Red in the inside, red on the outside. It's a 1958 Fury.

The car shakes. It takes on its persona. Just like that, its doors lock.

MICK AND DICK

My mother packed me lunches filled with candy canes, jelly beans, and Juicy Fruit when I was small. I'd get on the bus, feeling the heaviness of the lunches in my backpack, my mom practicing the can-can or some other dance for her Sweet Adelines conventions before sending me off.

My dad had a fascination with his tools—his leaf blower, stuff he used for welding. He'd be out in the machine shed, or out somewhere on a tractor, or maybe doing something with the cows in the barn.

I never really wanted trouble, so I'm not sure why mother was always saying to me, "Don't get yourself in trouble."

I liked to be at my friends' house—Mick and Dick, in their yard, swimming in their pond in the summer. They had two big dogs, also called Mick and Dick.

There were twin beds in their childhood bedroom. Crooked framed awards populated one wall—4-H firsts and seconds.

It was always Mick and Dick. She was Michele and he was Richard. Mick and Dick. Dick and Mick. I met them in kindergarten in a class with Mrs. Mahlik.

The last time I saw Mick was the time I slept with Dick and I did better than expected. I wasn't passionate. We were quiet in his bed, under his covers. I suppose Mick knew what we were after.

Until then, the three of us did everything together: we played on swings, hung upside-down from the baler. We took my dad's tractor out on joy rides. Mick was afraid of driving, so usually she just sat on the side, on the fender that went over one of the big tires. Or she stood in back. She was beautiful—with long blonde hair and these little spiky green eyes. Dick was a bit taller and his hair was coarse, and his cheeks were wide. They reminded me of Hansel and Gretel. They lived down the road from me—their dad worked at the paper mill thirty miles away, and their mom stayed home and smoked a lot of cigarettes. My dad was a farmer—and my mom did things like read the paper, cook desserts, do things with her singing group, and she rode her bike to Dick and Mick's to hang out with their mother.

The last time I saw Dick was after thirty years had passed. We sat roasting marshmallows over a fire that had grown to be enormous. He didn't ask about my dad or my mom.

I'd come back for my dad's funeral in Wisconsin. I asked about Mick.

From his telling it . . . he made his sister Mick sound like a rabbit in a trap, like meat. Like chicken.

IN THE REPORTS

Be your best self, says my dad to me in a dream.

In real life, he doesn't say this. He says things like, I'm sorry I was such a bad dad. Please don't tell anyone about me.

I wake to the rain, my stomach rumbling. Look out to the back yard at the peach tree I planted. I stub my toe on a chair leg.

I pee.

I start to wonder who my best self is, how to use the best of me. My regrets. Wishing some of my time back.

My son's married now. A soldier.

When I was young, a good friend was abducted. I was the last one, at least in the reports, who saw her.

I make myself some toast. My four dogs surround me and they stir. My partner, still in bed, talks in his sleep.

He says, Sacrifice, sacrifice, sacrifice.

COMPANION

The stillness of the elevator makes its occupants grow silent. A woman with curved hands holding a stability ball squeezes herself into a corner. A man stands wringing his cap the color of a kidney. Another, who holds the leash of his furry companion, donned with a harness labeling him as service, looks up to the ceiling. A man with no legs in a wheelchair wears the same kind of jungle hat another woman (a veteran herself) recognizes, like the one on her son's head in the picture he sent the day before, geared up in his flack vest, rifle on his chest, his face done up in black and green and brown. She says hello to the man. She looks at his eyes. She has so much to lose.

SPECIAL OPERATIONS

They entered the fort-like railway station with eyes like grains of sand. Some of the emblems on their uniforms were embroidered commando daggers. US Army Airborne Special Operations.

They wore combat boots. Most of them were shiny.

They were deferential. They wore their hair short. Some had none at all. Respect for regulation.

They carried duffel bags filled with underwear and t-shirts. They were fit. They drank from their canteens.

They held their phones. They wrote to their mothers, if they had them.

Some of them slept.

They took up most of the station.

WALKING THE DOG

Each night my son appears younger than he is now. Last night he was a baby. In my arms, in a boat. I felt the water, but thought he was above it. I pulled him up, finally. I had to breathe back into him.

Sometimes he's four or six or seven. Never the twenty that he is now, away and maybe not returning. I send him cards and sometimes checks. He calls, and says he has received them. I once had a dream he was a turtle, transformed. Like those Teenage Mutants. I denied he was my son though, until he came out of his shell with his face.

He was born on a Friday with early contractions. Our cord almost killed him. When I woke up someone said he was alive. I said please and thank you. I couldn't see him yet. I wanted something more to numb me.

One night, he was a soldier. He killed people, but said it was for the good of his nation. At night he smoked cigarettes. He talked, a baby again, crying right back into me.

He used to grab my leg. I hear children's voices everywhere, calling for all the mothers, all over.

One time he was disfigured. I took him to the doctor. But the doctor was my dad, and all my dad wanted to do was cry. He farted and burped, told me how fucked up I was. He tripped and fell over a patch of dried blood. My son laughed at that, and then he was a man with a girlfriend.

One night my dog ran off. I ran to find him, in a fisherman's wharf. I'd never been there before, not ever. My dog swam, and I swam to get him. He turned into a baby. He was mine, though it took me too long to know that.

I spend my worthwhile days mowing lawn, walking the dog and ironing some clothing. I'll dust and tear away at the laundry. I'll call my son and listen to his voicemail.

There was a time I told him Shh. Please, I'd said. I was tired then. I'm tired now, so I go to bed early, close my eyes, and here he is: face-to-face with me, as if I never left him.

FACE-DOWN

Once in the water, face down, I move my arms in a stroke. My legs kick. I lift my head with each rotation, slightly, out of the water: to the right, to the left, right and left, etcetera. I practice the front crawl. I push. I breathe. I sturdy myself. I blow out when my head's in. See and hear the gurgle. In order to keep myself aligned, when my head is down, my ears numbed by my swim cap, my eyes focused and behind the suction of my goggles, I stretch my arms and scoop, alternating sides, looking down to a straight pattern of blue cubes under and continually before me, warning me of each end with a T.

CANINE

"How's your heart rate?" says the doctor's assistant when I go there.

"You tell me," I say. I served in the medical field in the Air Force years ago. I have no diagnosis.

The day before I ate corn on the cob with my supposed soulmate, and swam—with our four canines—in our neighborhood pool. I sensed an elephant in the room, but also was aware of how cliché that sounded.

I chew on wads of gum at the office. One after another. My heart rate is just fine, my doctor assures me. It's just fine. I'm absolutely fine. I'm in the best shape of my life.

CATNIP

I fold the paper, waiting at the diner. Sip my water, check my phone for the time. The guy is late: my date, who I met online. I look out the window: the moon like clumps.

The paper has a picture of a guy wanted for killing someone in the tropics. The guy in the paper is bald with big eyebrows and a pug nose. I fold the paper into a plane. The lipstick-ed waitress brings me coffee, asks if I want more.

"Not yet," I say. "I'm waiting for my boyfriend."

I only talked to the guy I'm meeting once, while discussing arrangements. We exchanged a few emails, mostly him telling me how he specializes in catnip, adding herbs that are supposed to cure ailments: hairballs, overactive bladders, biting behaviors, things like that. He has five cats. He seems more attentive than most guys I date. In his picture he's red-haired, bearded, skinny. Cute. His name is Charlie.

I wear an orange sweater, my hair in a bun. That's how I told him he could find me.

I hear plates banging around in the kitchen. A man sits at the counter, sipping something. A woman and a babbling baby sit in the booth across. Other than that, the place is pretty empty. It smells like bacon.

A man enters, making the bell ring. He approaches me, asks if I am Stormy. "I'm Stormy," I say.

My name is really Elle.

He sits, says his name is Charlie. He looks nothing like his online picture: pointy-chinned and small-mouthed, big dark brows. I say, "Are you sure?"

He says he is. His voice is high-pitched and he has a Jersey accent. The more I look at him, the more I notice he looks like the wanted man on the flier. The fliers are everywhere. I unfold my airplane to sneak another look.

He asks if I'm hungry. I tell him I am starving.

The waitress comes to asks what we want. She writes on her tablet, chewing her gum. I get tomato soup and he orders tuna.

When the waitress leaves, I ask Charlie if he's been anywhere warm recently. He says no. He says he's from Jersey.

He has a nice smile. His nose isn't as pugged at the man in his profile. He looks kind of cat-like, his ears pointy, his tongue long. He licks his lips a lot.

He makes a sound like a purr.

Another man enters, then another. They look alike, like Charlie. They sit at the counter. Fill the booths. They all wear vests and Wranglers. Stray animal hairs stick to their backs and arms and middles.

I ask Charlie who he is.

He narrows his eyes. He sticks his tongue out.

I laugh at him and I hiss.

DOG-FACED

After his hacking cough sends him to the ER, his brain fooling him back into thinking he is dying, he sits in his gown on the papered table, letting the pregnant nurse come to take his vitals: the cuff around his arm, letting the machine pump, the clip over his finger for his heart rate, in a race, and the thing in his ear that beeps and tells her what his temp is, which to him is a flame erupting from his center, rising up and out every pore and crevice. The nurse doesn't really say much. But when she takes back her devices, writing on her clipboard, he turns around to the machine to see the numbers.

"That's mine?" he says.

She smiles in her happy-dog-faced scrubs, says nothing, and she nods.

"It's usually not that high," he says.

She says sometimes coming here makes people nervous.

After she leaves, he sits alone, coughing up air that he imagines is infected. Like the stone in his chest that for days now has been stuck there. He coughs more, thinking of what the nurse said. He's not nervous. He used to work in places like this, and it's always the same, whether in New York or Wisconsin, New Jersey or Ohio, even at the army hospitals in Germany: drawing blood from infants, with the bio-hazard pails and latex, the gauze and pads of alcohol and Band-Aids. He's in a state he isn't used to, an out-of-towner, and the only way his insurance will pay is if he resorts to the ER. He told the lady at check-in it wasn't even urgent, talking in his voice that lately he doesn't recognize. He's so hoarse. It's strange to hear his voice, in its altered state—how could it sound so shallow—this voice that makes him feel like he isn't the man he's meant to be, one who married once then twice—he did not mean to leave his wife and children.

He hears a baby crying in the next room, or rather, the next curtain over. It's a quiet day, he thinks, for the ER, but it's a small town, early in the morning, and he knows from all the hospitals he's worked at, that the small ones usually mean you might be gifted with a shorter wait time.

In the corner of the room, he thinks he sees a peep of his from a former workplace, a man who used to work in triage, how the man ran out into a load of shrapnel, like all those other men, the blood on their hands and arms and faces.

He thinks about war. It's in the news, up there on the screen, out there in the waiting room, up there on the TV.

The war. The war. He's never been at war, or has he?

He gets up and adjusts the table. He puts a blanket over him and looks up at the ceiling, but that only makes him cough more.

He sits up again, hearing the baby next to him crying more and more and more and more and more, like the girl he's visiting this week, here, in this state, how she cried into his arms when she told him she was pregnant. It's OK, he said, holding her, feeling his heart get hotter, his breath rising from inside, his illness, his sickness: the germs.

I TOOK ONE OF HER LEGS

Back at the hotel lobby, the pleasure of the first cold beer was wrecked by our feeling vomitus and stinky. We straggled to the hotel after the race, the last guy on our team looking pale, like he was about to keel over.

Still, we kept upright for the pictures, did the thing where we smiled, held up our medals. There were eleven of us, and one guy did two legs, so he held up two of his medals. The backs of all the medals said something unique: the parts of them, put together, solving a puzzle. As if, after two hundred miles, our team could even think straight.

We all loved dogs. So we called our team the Dog Legs, wore our matching T-shirts with an assortment of dogs and legs, and we even decorated our two vans with all things dog-like. During the race, we barked a lot.

At the hotel, we ordered Goldens. We were in Niagara Falls. There was nothing portentous about it. The waiter put napkins under our beers. We sat looking at the beers for a while, undermining the quality of them, or of this moment, which we had talked about—assumed—during the whole race would be special.

I lived just south, sixty miles tops. Two of my colleagues, who lived within thirty miles of me, lived a lot closer. The other folks traveled all the way from Ohio, one from Massachusetts. One from Albany. The only two guys from our team lived in other countries. Tom lived in Brazil. Jay lived in Toronto. We had two vans. It was a Ragnar.

The race started in Cobourg, Ontario. We had to drive to get there, and shuttle run the rest of the way. We went day and night. Sleeping in our bags in parks. At any given time, at least one of our team members was running. We'd get in the van and go, go, go. Run,

run, run. Always, across all these many miles, we'd see all these people running.

I did better than I expected. I took the baton when it was my turn. I crossed fields in the daytime, and at night, I filtered through the late bar-life streets of Mississauga, where folks stood drinking and smoking legal pot on the sidewalk.

I only covered eighteen miles, on my own feet, running. We came and went, we came and went, we got in the van. I drove part of the way.

I got lost, not only driving.

We slept. We ran. We ate. We slept in sleeping bags in the open air in the middle of Toronto. We pooped in port-a-potties. I brought the toilet paper. Stuff fell out of the van. It's like living in a purse, said one of my teammates.

One of the girls was injured, so I took one of her legs.

Stacy was from Massachusetts. My friend Ann was from New Jersey.

We panted. We said woof.

We brushed our teeth on the sidewalk.

SPIFF AND ME

The first night of the auction, there was a double rainbow.

This was after storms blew things across the yard, and the porta potty—there for the next day's auction—fell over.

The rest of the family went to the site where the valuables were auctioned: things like antiques and jewelry. Furniture. Old dolls and the sewing machine my grandmother used to patch up all of our old clothing. Lamps. I'm not even sure what exactly went because I was the one to stay behind at the farm to make sure no one came along to steal the stuff on the lawn.

All over the yard, things were assembled: chairs and boxes of utensils. An old washing machine. Blankets. Rugs. The crib my mom used to sleep in. And me, too. In one of the sheds was a piano. Church pews. A bench.

The front of the machine shed was lined with rows of tractors. A lawn mower. Inside the machine shed were tables filled with bins of dishes. Tools. Tires. Old radios. Appliances and hoses.

I'd been at the farm all week, having driven from New York with my dog Spiff. I had my hybrid bike on a rack on the back of my Toyota. We drove through Canada, across Michigan, then took the ferry from Ludington into Sturgeon Bay, Wisconsin. It's a ferry ride I know, mostly from the four years I lived in Michigan. This time I had Spiff in his dog seat, and left him in the car—there's a special section in the ferry for vehicles with dogs—where they can get a lot of air and proper circulation.

My last time at this farm was after my Uncle Carl died. In February—I carried his ashes down the aisle with my cousin. Carl was godfather to us both. Carl owned the house that used to belong to my grandparents and their grandparents. It's where my mom grew up. Where I spent a lot of time, when I was growing up, too.

The day after the funeral, I went into the house with my mom and her siblings, my sister and her husband, and our other cousins.

We wore gloves and facemasks. Tried to bring down cobwebs. Dead bugs sticking to the webs. The blinds in all the rooms were shriveled. We took sheets away to get laundered. We went through boxes of papers. We swept. We cleaned. We dusted.

The house was huge: made of seven bedrooms, a parlor, and a den. A living room, a dining room, a kitchen. Two bathrooms, a mudroom. A big kind of lounge upstairs. And closets big enough to be rooms of their own. The attic. And every room was full. Every closet, every drawer, contained stuff.

My last time at the farm before that was probably before my grandma died. She died the same year I got my degree from Southern Mississippi. Her funeral was on the day of my graduation. Instead of walking across the stage, I was at her funeral. I drove up from Mississippi with my son, and my uncle Carl, the one who ended up running the farm, walked with me through the cemetery, offering me tissues. My grandmother, I learned, was buried next to my childhood sweetheart, who shot himself in his early twenties. I had known about his death, had heard about it after it happened, but I didn't know his plot was next to my grandma. And where my grandfather would later be buried, and later, the ashes of my uncle.

After my grandma died, my uncle had their dog Lou euthanized. I'm not sure why. My grandfather went into assisted living. My uncle took over the farm. He rarely invited anybody over.

Most of my other family members lived nearby. I opted to stay at the house during this last visit. I brought a cot, and stayed in the room that used to belong to my mother. The room where I used to sleep when I'd visit.

Of course this time, it was mostly empty. I vacuumed it. I spread out my cot. I brought a dog bed for Spiff.

By the first night of the auction, we were pretty much set. I was tired. We all were. There was my mom, my aunt Blue, my uncle Sal, and their spouses. My cousins and my sister. They were all at the auction site.

I was the only one here. Just Spiff and me.

I sat outside on one of the sofas to be auctioned. There'd been a hole that my family had hired someone to dig. Where we threw stuff, like the chair where my uncle died, because it wasn't salvageable. We had the hole covered before the auction for liability reasons. All the animals were sold by now, save the wild cats that still came around.

I was still in awe by what was left of my grandma's garden. I remembered helping her harvest cucumbers, and tomatoes. Sprouts of rhubarb still came up. Asparagus and onions. I picked them, cut them, tried to cook them and use what I could with what was left of the kitchen.

But on this night a storm came. It blew everything all over. It rained and it thundered. I tried to call members of my family, but no one was answering,

HOW DOGS EXPERIENCE THE WORLD

I smelled the sweat of myself—in the oversized fuchsia tank I bought the week before at the local Dollar Store, where the smell there was stale and cold—the smell of a warehouse, save maybe the aisle filled with candles. That was just after having driven from Buffalo, New York, through Canada and Customs, taking the ferry from Ludington, MI, to Sturgeon Bay, WI, then to Green Bay, a route I'd taken several times before, this time with my dog, Spiff.

I'd read a lot about how dogs experience the world with their noses, and I wondered then, how this world smelled to him.

Spiff mostly stayed inside, because it was so hot out.

I wondered if he smelled the death smells—my uncle died there just four months before. Years before, my grandma died in her sleep on her day bed.

While going through one of the drawers from the many upstairs dressers, I found a collection of black-and-white pictures of dead people in caskets. When I asked my mom, who was there with me getting ready for the auction, she said it was probably someone in the family—that back in those days, our ancestors used to have wakes at the house, in the parlor.

But people were also born there. Over sixty years before, one of my mom's fifty-some cousins took his first breath in the same room where my grandmother took her last. That cousin, Bob, was there, at the auction, on a rented golf cart. Cancer ate at his bones, and it was just an ordeal for him to get there.

I remember the smell of manure, the smell of butchering chickens, plucking the feathers—burnt skin. The smell of my grandpa making breakfast. The smell of the chalk on the board in the common area where us kids—my many second cousins—would play school, sitting on desks that must've come from someone's town hall classroom. The smell of the basement, playing pool there, the smell of the cue. The smell of popcorn: when my aunt still lived there and would babysit for my sister and me.

The smell of curry, from a dish I made just a few days before, using vegetables my ancestors planted, and though the garden hadn't been tended to in ages, these dear things still made their appearance. As I cooked, I added spices I'd brought, savoring the smell of cumin, a balance of fennel, ginger, garlic. I tasted as I went. I sipped the broth, and when I asked my mom if maybe she would like some, she took one taste, and said it was too salty.

Now the place smells like lots and lots of people. Outside groups of farmers with hats and work shoes move in a pattern, following the auctioneer from wagon to wagon, tractor to tractor, from one plank filled with stuff to the next one. It smells different than my last farm auction, the home where I grew up, after my parent's divorce and my father's nervous breakdown. I was thirteen when that happened

It's thirty-four years later.

I sit here with that, holding my dog Spiff. He's a rescue. I pet his thick fur. He pants. He tilts his head and looks up at me with his little bulging eyes. His mouth is so small. His breath is like magic.